JASMINE
HAS
SOMETHING TO SHARE

Children Book

Written

by Deborah J Arnold

CREDITS:

ACKNOWLEDGEMENTS

Thanking God for His grace.

To my gift of friends and family members:

special thanks to Kinaya for editing.

I embrace a legacy of faith to my grandchildren, and their children's children to have a future an expected end.

Margaret Graham who prayed that my children's book writing will come to pass.

PREFACE

This book "Jasmine Has Something to share" is inspired by one of my granddaughters when she was three years old and elementary school age.

First, I noticed that Jasmine would constantly change into her princess dresses within minutes. It happened so often, that you had to notice. Jasmine would be in her own world. Her own princess world with movement of her lips softly speaking in her own imagination. What imagination would lead her to change into different color princess dresses?

She will glow if you tell her she is a princess. And there were times she would still glow from a sad day.

She loved to dance from dance videos with style with her sisters. She had to have her own princess dress up in order to dance. And she is a character.

Jasmine was in a ballet class in Georgia, where she attended dance lessons. This art of ballet enhanced her character.

Jasmine woke up a little late, rising, arms rising, and stretching.

"Oh I had a dream!"

In the kitchen mother is cooking and preparing breakfast.

Jasmine said, " Mother, I have something to share."

Mother replied, " I am cooking and preparing breakfast. Let us sit down later together and have time and share."

" Yes, mother indeed." Jasmine said.

After breakfast, Jasmine went back to her bedroom and looked around. Jasmine says, "I can not wait until a later time to share with my mother!"

"I will go to my second oldest sister and share with her, Jasmine thought."

Jasmine went to her second oldest sister's room. Her sister was tall with a basketball in her hand and a backpack on her back.

Jasmine said to her second oldest sister, "I have something to share! Do you have time to chat, because I must tell you about my dream?"

Jasmine's second oldest sister replied, "I do not have time, Jasmine. It is time to go to my practice."

The honking of a car's horn is heard. Honk, Honk!

"My ride's here. I must go, Bye, Bye!"

"Mmm," sounds Jasmine with her finger over her mouth.

Jasmine thought to herself. "I can hardly wait for time with my mother. In the meantime, I will go to my oldest sister's room and ask her for time to hear my dream. She will have a moment for me."

Jasmine wandered into her oldest sister's room, "I have something to share. Do you have time to chat about my dream?"

The oldest sister is applying makeup in the mirror.

She said, "My apologies, I am dressing and applying my makeup. I must get ready for dance practice and my photoshoot."

Again, Jasmine thought to herself, "I must share my dream because I can not wait for my mother."

Jasmine went to the third oldest sister to share with her.

"I have something to share. Can we chat for a moment? I had a dream."

With humor, the third sister replied, "My apologies Jasmine, but I am busy. I am chatting and laughing with my friends on my cell phone."

Then her third sister returned back to her phone to chat and laugh with her friends.

Jasmine stood in the hallway of their home, feeling a sigh with her hand on her head.

Then she said, " I will not wait, because I must share."

Jasmine had no one to share her dream with. What was she going to do?

Then Jasmine heard her name called. "Jasmine, Jasmine! Where are you?"

"It's my mother's voice!" Jasmine noticed. "I have refreshments," mother replied. "Are you ready to have time and share? Please meet me on the lanai!"

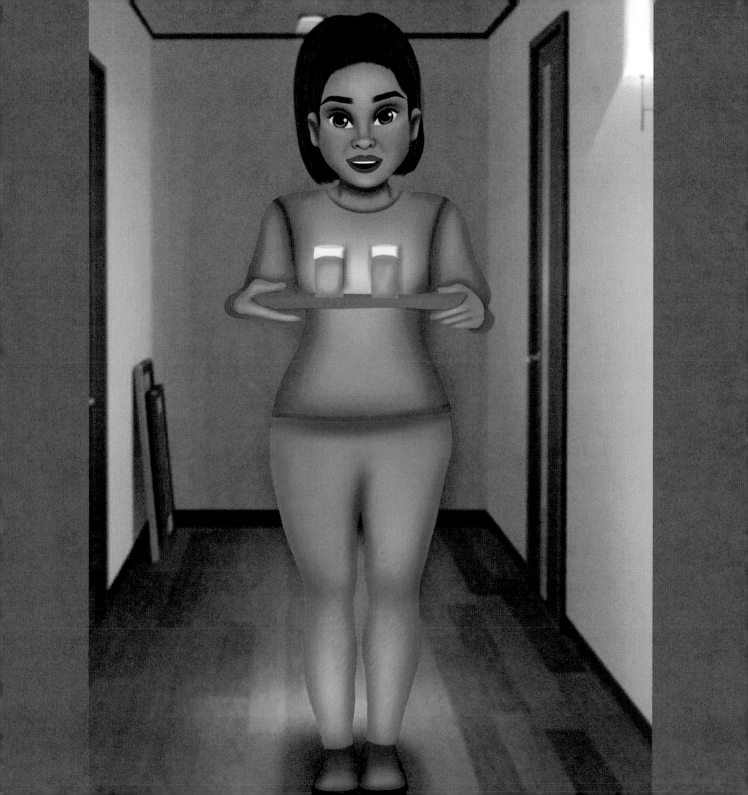

"It was exciting to know the time has come to have time and share with my mother, Jasmine thought." Within minutes, Jasmine quickly changed her clothes and ran to meet mother on the lanai.

Oh, what joy Jasmine had to chat with mother when the time came to share.

Mother and Jasmine sat comfortably on the outside furniture with tea cakes and juice.

Jasmine said, "Mother, I had a dream to share and I want to understand."

Mother answered, "share your dream with me."

Jasmine paused, and then said , "First, I must confess. I did not wait for our time to share. I tried to go before you because I was impatient. I asked my second oldest sister, my first oldest sister, and my third sister for time to share, but they were busy. I could not wait to share my dream, after you told me until later. My sisters had no time to chat, and it was disappointing.

If I had waited as asked, it would have saved me from my feelings being hurt."

Mother replied, " Patience is strength that God gives us. It assists us to value time . It is Not thinking solely of itself and being upset because of the waiting time.

If you had waited on mother, your feelings probably would not be hurt."

Jasmine: Yes, Mother indeed.

Jasmine smiled.

"Jasmine, now tell me your dream," mother said softly."

"Yes, mother. In my dream, I saw a tree. It reached heaven, and I could not wait to climb it. This tree was very tall, beautiful with nice and friendly branches to climb. It reached up to the sky, through the clouds and far away to heaven. It had a glow of light at the top of it. I felt a peace about this tree in my dream. It looked fun to climb."

Then Jasmine genuinely asked, " Mother, will you assist me to understand my dream?"

Mother shared and said, "there was a dreamer named Joseph. God gave him a dream about his future, and he was excited. Joseph had hard things to do in his life.

However, he kept his trust and patience in God. Joseph's dream came true with a fulfilled life and blessing to all. Forgivable, his siblings received goodness.

Jasmine, God's thoughts and plans for you are good, hope, a future and not harm. Have love by caring and giving. Be courageous by doing the right thing with honesty and respect daily. You are beautifully and wonderfully made so love you. Know that God loves you and will be with you.

God gave Jacob the father of Joseph a dream of God's promise too and the blessings continued.

Now, start climbing to the top of your dreams."

Mother and Jasmine are happy and enjoying each other with time and share.

The End

<u>REFERENCE</u>

Jeremiah 29:11 NIV
Genesis 37 NIV
Genesis 28 NIV
Galatians 5:22 NIV

Educational chat

1. Jasmine had a _____, and wanted to share it.
2. Who did she try to share her dream to? _____
3. Why did Jasmine ask her sisters to chat about her dream, after Mother asked her to wait? _____.
4. Jasmine had a dream about a _____? Explain? Describe?
5. Did Jasmine wish to climb the tree and why_____.
6. God's _____, and plans for you are _____, a _____, _____ , and not harm, an _____ Jeremiah 29:11.
7. Now, knowing God's thoughts for the future, what are your dreams? _____
8. Will you share with your parents, or guardians about your dream and ask to assist in overseeing it? _____
9. Who had a dream and kept the faith, trust in God and it came true_____?
10. Sometimes school or homework is hard, will it assist us toward our goals and dreams? _____

ABOUT AUTHOR

Deborah J. Arnold is a mother of one daughter and four grandchildren. A native of Atlanta, Georgia, U.S.A. She earned her education at Georgia State University, Georgia, and Liberty Christian University, Virginia.

My hope and faith was to help myself by assisting others. One of my steps toward my dreams were singing songs, and sharing time with nieces, nephews, and my grandchildren. This inspiration brought me to embrace writing a children's book.

"The end of something is better than its beginning. Patience is better than pride." Ecclesiastes 7:8

Contact **deborahnote1@gmail.com**/ Jean Arnold /Facebook/ Instagram

JASMINE HAS SOMETHING TO SHARE, was written to motivate reading, dreams, and patience. A Faith based book.

Here is one of my writing genres of children's books JASMINE HAS SOMETHING TO SHARE This book writing is an encouragement to grandparents, parents, students, and me to open up their hidden talents. Believe in your Dreams and Legacy. Warmest thanks, D.J.A.

DEBORAH J ARNOLD

Made in the USA
Columbia, SC
23 November 2022

71567984R00024